来自夏令营的信

【美】露西·瑞切·潘纳◎著
【美】佩姬·比林-弗莱◎绘
范晓星◎译

天津出版传媒集团
新蕾出版社

献给奈奥米·克莱恩。

——露西·瑞切·潘纳

图书在版编目（CIP）数据

来自夏令营的信/(美)潘纳(Penner,L.R.)著；
(美)比林-弗莱(Billin-Frye,P.)绘；范晓星译.—
天津:新蕾出版社,2015.3(2024.12 重印)
(数学帮帮忙·互动版)
书名原文:Clean-Sweep Campers
ISBN 978-7-5307-6209-7

Ⅰ.①来…　Ⅱ.①潘…②比…③范…　Ⅲ.①数学–
儿童读物　Ⅳ.①O1–49

中国版本图书馆 CIP 数据核字(2015)第 037084 号

Clean-Sweep Campers by Lucille Recht Penner;
Illustrated by Paige Billin-Frye.

Copyright © 2000 by Kane Press, Inc.

All rights reserved, including the right of reproduction in whole or in part in any form. This edition published by arrangement with Kane Press, Inc. New York, NY, represented by Lerner Publishing Group through The ChoiceMaker Korea Co. agency.

Simplified Chinese translation copyright © 2015 by New Buds Publishing House (Tianjin) Limited Company

ALL RIGHTS RESERVED

本书中文简体版专有出版权经由中华版权代理中心授予新蕾出版社(天津)有限公司。未经许可,不得以任何方式复制或抄袭本书的任何部分。

津图登字:02-2012-220

出版发行:天津出版传媒集团
　　　　　新蕾出版社
http://www.newbuds.com.cn

地　　址:天津市和平区西康路 35 号(300051)
出 版 人:马玉秀
电　　话:总编办 (022)23332422
　　　　　发行部 (022)23332679　23332351
传　　真:(022)23332422
经　　销:全国新华书店
印　　刷:天津新华印务有限公司
开　　本:787mm×1092mm　1/16
印　　张:3
版　　次:2015 年 3 月第 1 版　2024 年 12 月第 22 次印刷
定　　价:12.00 元

无处不在的数学

资深编辑　卢　江

　　人们常说"兴趣是最好的老师",有了兴趣,学习就会变得轻松愉快。数学对于孩子来说或许有些难,因为比起语文,数学显得枯燥、抽象,不容易理解,孩子往往不那么喜欢。可许多家长都知道,学数学对于孩子的成长和今后的生活有多么重要。不仅数学知识很有用,学习数学过程中获得的数学思想和方法更会影响孩子的一生,因为数学素养是构成人基本素质的一个重要因素。但是,怎样才能让孩子对数学产生兴趣呢? 怎样才能激发他们兴致勃勃地去探索数学问题呢? 我认为,让孩子读些有趣的书或许是不错的选择。读了这套"数学帮帮忙",我立刻产生了想把它们推荐给教师和家长朋友们的愿望,因为这真是一套会让孩子爱上数学的好书!

　　这套有趣的图书从美国引进,原出版者是美国资深教育专家。每本书讲述一个孩子们生活中的故事,由故事中出现的问题自然地引入一个数学知识,然后通过运用数学知识解决问题。比如,从帮助外婆整理散落的纽扣引出分类,从为小狗记录藏骨头的地点引出空间方位等等。故事素材全部来源于孩子们的真实生活,不是童话,不是幻想,而是鲜活的生活实例。正是这些发生在孩子身边的故事,让孩子们懂得,数学无处不在并且非常有用;这些鲜活的实例也使得抽象的概念更易于理解,更容易激发孩子学习数学的兴趣,让他们逐渐爱上数学。这样的教育思想和方法与我国近年来提倡的数学教育理念是十分吻合的!

这是一套适合5~8岁孩子阅读的书,书中的有趣情节和生动的插画可以将抽象的数学问题直观化、形象化,为孩子的思维活动提供具体形象的支持。如果亲子共读的话,家长可以带领孩子推测情节的发展,探讨解决难题的办法,让孩子在愉悦的氛围中学到知识和方法。

值得教师和家长朋友们注意的是,在每本书的后面,出版者还加入了"互动课堂"及"互动练习",一方面通过一些精心设计的活动让孩子巩固新学到的数学知识,进一步体会知识的含义和实际应用;另一方面帮助家长指导孩子阅读,体会故事中数学之外的道理,逐步提升孩子的阅读理解能力。

我相信孩子读过这套书后一定会明白,原来,数学不是烦恼,不是包袱,数学真能帮大忙!

亲爱的爸爸妈妈：

　　我在夏令营过得太开心了！我很喜欢宿舍里的小伙伴，也喜欢游泳、画画和做手工。只有一件事我不喜欢，就是打扫卫生。我们每天都要整理房间，为什么？我这就来告诉你们。

我们这间小木屋里总共住了 8 个人。哦，等一下，应该是 10 个人，我们的两位辅导员基特和嘉琪，也住在这里。

　　所以，这么多人住在一起，屋子很快就变得乱七八糟了。我才不在乎呢，其他孩子也一样。

可辅导员说她们有个好主意,能让打扫房间变得充满乐趣。好吧,我就喜欢有趣的事!

爱你们的乖女儿 安妮

另:请把我的哥斯拉面具寄来好吗?

亲爱的爸爸妈妈:

　　得,原来乐趣就是分组!

　　基特和嘉琪把我们 8 个孩子分成了 2
组。每组的人数一样多,每组 4 个人。

然后，嘉琪在屋子正中央画了一条看不见的线，将宿舍一分为二。

　　我的朋友朱迪和我用袜子在地上摆了一条分界线，可辅导员说太乱了！袜子弄脏了，我们还得洗袜子，再整整齐齐地晾好！

　　一肚子牢骚！

言归正传，辅导员让我们每个组每天早上
分别打扫一半房间。这可算不上有趣的事。

　　打扫完毕，我们就去游泳了。

　　一半孩子在天使鱼队，另一半在金鱼队。我在天使鱼队。我们游得棒极了。

　　我爱你们，亲亲！

安妮

　　另：给我寄些饼干吧。

亲爱的爸爸妈妈：

　　你们肯定猜不到发生了什么事。

　　我们把浴室给忘了！

　　哪个组也不愿意打扫，哪怕一个组一半呢。
我们的活儿已经够多了。所以说把我们分成两
个组，把宿舍分成两半是没用的，我们还需要
一个组。

我想到一个好主意，而且事实证明，这个主意很不错！

"我们大家平均分成 3 组。"我说，"每组人数都占 $\frac{1}{3}$。一组打扫浴室，另外两组还是平分打扫宿舍。"

嗯,主意是不赖。可随即托碧说我没法把8
个人平均分成3组。

　　我们都不知道该怎么办。我说，或许我们
该把妈妈们都请到夏令营来帮我们打扫卫生
吧。哈哈！我是开玩笑呢！

　　托碧说："如果有一个辅导员肯帮忙呢？那
么我们就有9个人了。9个人平分3组很容易，
每组3个人。"

你们猜怎么样？基特和嘉琪都不肯！

哦，不好，我游泳要迟到了。我要走了。天使
鱼队将成为胜利鱼队！

爱你们！

安妮

另：我的小乌龟们怎么样了？别忘了，它们
喜欢你们用手喂它们吃小虫子。

亲爱的爸爸妈妈：

　　我再接着告诉你们后来发生的事吧。因为我还是觉得分成 3 组的主意很好，我就提议："如果每个小组 2 个人呢？这样就有 2 个人剩出来没事做。"

嗯,大家倒是不介意被剩下。可你们猜怎么样?没有人愿意打扫,个个都想被剩下没事做!

所以，我们决定干脆平均分成 4 个小组。每个小组都是 2 个人。

　　第一组打扫一半小木屋。

　　第二组打扫另一半。

第三组打扫浴室。我被分在这组，太幸运了！

第四组负责清理门廊附近的杂草。

可是问题又来了。不光是有做卫生的问题，金鱼队游得比我们天使鱼队快。呜呜。

你们伤心的女儿　安妮

另:再多寄些饼干来吧！

亲爱的爸爸妈妈：

你们想知道为什么我们分 4 组的计划也没有成功吗？

因为有蜜蜂！

负责拔草的一个小姑娘被蜜蜂蜇了。她们俩就罢工了！我们还得想办法。

我们一边想着办法，一边比赛侧手翻。太棒了，我能翻到一半！

就在我头朝下的时候，朱迪突然说："我知道该怎么做了！"

朱迪眉飞色舞地说："我们可以分成 8 组，我们宿舍一共是 8 个人，每个人就是 $\frac{1}{8}$ 。我们每个人都是一个小组！"

　　这个主意多了不起！这样的话每个人都
可以做她最喜欢的事情了。

奈奥米喜欢打扫,她负责地面卫生。托碧和乔喜欢洗洗涮涮,她俩把洗脸池和花洒擦得亮堂堂的。朱迪则是个除尘高手,她居然还带着羽毛掸子来夏令营了!

每个人都有一份自己最喜欢的工作！

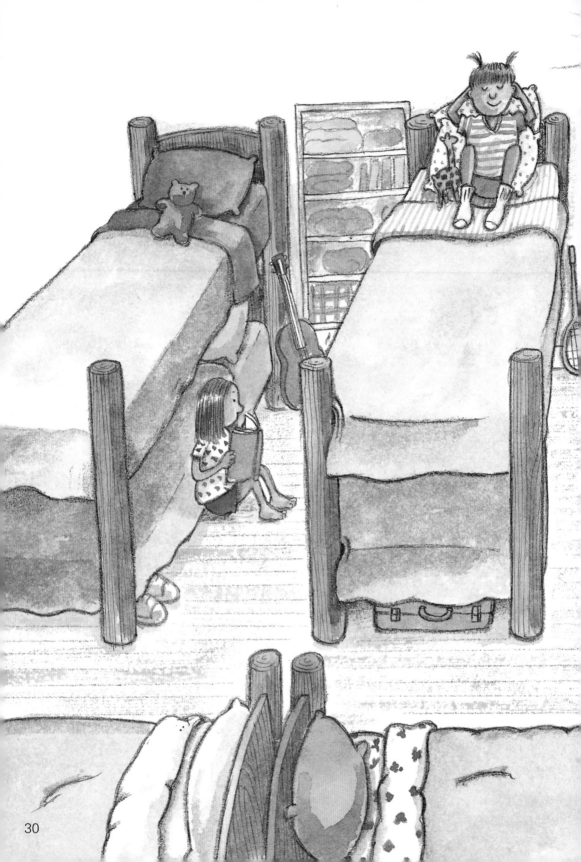

现在，夏令营里的每件事我都喜欢，连打扫卫生也喜欢！

你们亲爱的女儿　安妮

另：可我还是不喜欢打扫自己的房间！

31

分 数

运动会开始了！试一试把 12 个小营员平均分组吧。

有好几种方法呢。

1.分 2 组　　　　　　　平均分 2 组

$\dfrac{1}{2}$　　　　　　　$\dfrac{2}{2}$

说一说,为什么 12 个小营员的 $\dfrac{1}{2}$ 是 6 个人。

2.分 3 组　　　　　　　平均分 3 组

$\dfrac{1}{3}$　　　　　　$\dfrac{2}{3}$　　　　　　$\dfrac{3}{3}$

说一说,为什么 12 个小营员的 $\dfrac{2}{3}$ 是 8 个人。

3.分 4 组　　　　　　　平均分 4 组

$\dfrac{1}{4}$　　　　$\dfrac{2}{4}$　　　　$\dfrac{3}{4}$　　　　$\dfrac{4}{4}$

说一说,为什么 12 个小营员的 $\dfrac{3}{4}$ 是 9 个人。

亲爱的家长朋友，请您和孩子一起完成下面这些内容，会有更大的收获哟！

提高阅读能力

- 看看封面，和孩子讨论一下标题，这本书会是一个什么样的故事？
- 读完第 3~5 页，可以给孩子指出来，这个故事是以书信的形式写成的。请孩子想一想，写信的人是谁？信又是写给谁的？请孩子分享一下他在夏令营、在家或在学校打扫卫生的经历。他觉得有意思吗？为什么？
- 读完这个故事，请孩子给安妮写封信吧。

巩固数学概念

- 在阅读故事的同时,和孩子一起检查一下安妮计算的分数是否正确。

- 利用第 32 页的图表,请孩子数一数每组分数代表几个孩子。问问孩子,如果要把小营员平均分成 6 组,每组会有几个人?

- 在第 15 页上,和孩子讨论一下,为什么 8 不可以平均分成 3 份?

- 和孩子复习故事里提到的平均分,$\frac{1}{2}$,$\frac{1}{3}$,$\frac{1}{4}$ 和 $\frac{1}{8}$。请孩子用它们造一句话吧。

- 根据故事和插图,想一些数学问题考考孩子,比如:安妮的小木屋里有几张床?如果安妮和朱迪把每个女孩的一双袜子摆在地上,一共有几只袜子?

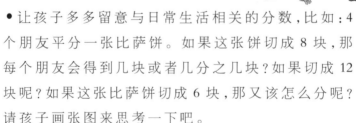

生活中的数学

- 让孩子多多留意与日常生活相关的分数,比如:4 个朋友平分一张比萨饼。如果这张饼切成 8 块,那每个朋友会得到几块或者几分之几块?如果切成 12 块呢?如果这张比萨饼切成 6 块,那又该怎么分呢?请孩子画张图来思考一下吧。

- 拿出绘图格纸和彩色铅笔,让孩子在纸上画一些正方形和三角形,把它们平均分成 2 份,3 份和 4 份。帮助孩子把每个部分用分数表示出来,比如:$\frac{1}{2}$,$\frac{1}{3}$,$\frac{1}{4}$。

涂一涂

请你选择自己喜欢的颜色，涂出下列图形的 $\frac{1}{2}$ 。

怎样涂出它的 $\frac{1}{2}$ 呢？

下面的分数能表示图中的涂色部分吗？能表示的画"√"，不能表示的画"×"。

$\frac{1}{2}$ （ ）

$\frac{1}{3}$ （ ）

$\frac{1}{4}$ （ ）

$\frac{1}{5}$ （ ）

折纸游戏

折出一张正方形纸的 $\frac{1}{4}$，你有几种折法？

你有什么好的办法吗？

请你来判断

安妮和朱迪各买了一个面包,一个大一个小。她俩各吃了 $\frac{1}{2}$ 个面包,她们吃得同样多,对吗?

我吃得多!

不对,我吃得多!

你发现了什么?

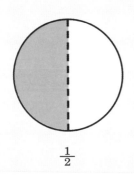

$\frac{1}{2}$

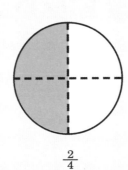

$\frac{2}{4}$

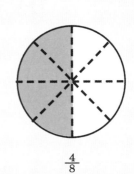

$\frac{4}{8}$

仔细观察以上三幅图,说说你的发现。

谁喝的水多？

同样的两杯水，基特和嘉琪各取了一杯，基特喝了一杯水的 $\frac{1}{4}$，嘉琪喝了一杯水的 $\frac{1}{3}$，谁喝得多？

A.嘉琪　　B.基特

谁的眼睛最亮？

看图回答问题。

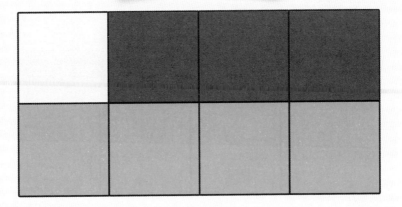

(1) 红色部分占整个图形的( )。

(2) 蓝色部分占整个图形的( )。

(3) 黄色部分占整个图形的( )。

互动练习1:

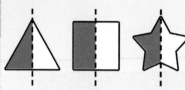

互动练习2:

$\dfrac{1}{2}$（√） $\dfrac{1}{3}$（×）

$\dfrac{1}{4}$（√） $\dfrac{1}{5}$（×）

互动练习3:

我们为你提供了4种折法:

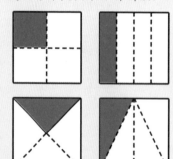

互动练习4:

　　不对,安妮的面包比较大,她吃得多。

互动练习5:

两幅图的阴影面积一样大。

$\dfrac{1}{2} = \dfrac{2}{4} = \dfrac{4}{8}$

互动练习6:

A. 嘉琪

互动练习7:

(1) 红色部分占整个图形的 $\dfrac{3}{8}$。

(2) 蓝色部分占整个图形的 $\dfrac{4}{8}$。

(3) 黄色部分占整个图形的 $\dfrac{1}{8}$。

（习题设计:杨　鑫）

Clean-Sweep Campers

Dear Mom and Dad,

It's terrific here! I like ALL the girls in my bunk and I love swimming and arts and crafts. There's only one thing I don't like—cleaning up. And we have to do it every single day. Why? I'll tell you.

We have eight people in this one little cabin. No, wait, make that ten. Our two counselors, Kit and Jackie, sleep here too.

So it gets messy pretty fast with all those people around. I don't mind the mess, and most of the girls feel the same way.

But the counselors say they have a great idea to make cleaning up fun. That's okay with me. I like fun!

Lots of love,

Annie

P.S. Would you please send my Godzilla mask?

Dear Mom and Dad,

Well, the fun turned out to be teams.

Kit and Jackie divided the eight of us into halves. So we were two equal teams. Four girls on each team.

Then Jackie divided the bunk in half by drawing an imaginary line right through the middle.

My friend Judy and I made a real line out of socks, but the counselors said it was messy. The socks got all dirty, so we had to wash them and put them away—neatly!

Grumble. Groan.

Anyway, the counselors had one team clean half the bunk each morning while the other team cleaned the other half. That wasn't what I call fun.

After clean-up, we go swimming.

Half the kids are Angelfish and half are Goldfish. I'm an Angelfish. We are COOL.

Love and kisses,

Annie

P.S. Send cookies.

Dear Mom and Dad,

You won't believe what happened.

We forgot about the bathroom!

Neither team wanted to clean even half the bathroom. We had enough work already. So dividing us and the bunk in half didn't work. We needed another team.

I had a good idea. Actually, it was great.

"Let's divide into three equal teams," I said. "Each team will be a third. One team will clean the bathroom. One team will clean half of the bunk. And one team will clean the other half."

Well, it WAS a great idea. But then Toby said that you can't divide eight people into three equal teams.

We still didn't know what to do. I said maybe we should ask our moms to come and clean up for us. Ha! Ha! Just kidding.

Toby said, "What if a counselor helps? Then we'll have nine people. It's easy to divide nine into thirds—three on a team."

Guess what? Kit and Jackie both said no.

Oh gosh, I'm late for swimming. Got to go. The Angelfish are about to become the Winnerfish!

Love,

Annie

P.S. How are my turtles? Don't forget, they like to eat worms out of your hand.

Dear Mom and Dad,

Here's what happened next. I still liked the idea of three teams. I suggested, "What if we had three teams of two girls each? Then two girls could be leftovers."

Well, the leftovers didn't mind a bit. But guess what? It turned out no one wanted to be on a team. Everyone wanted to be a leftover.

So we decided to divide into fourths. We could have two girls on each team—four equal teams.

The first team would clean half the cabin.

The second team would clean the other half.

The third team would clean the bathroom. I was on that team. Lucky me.

The fourth team would pull weeds near the porch.

It didn't work out. And not only that. The Goldfish beat the Angelfish.

Boo hoo.

Your sad daughter,

Annie

P.S. Please send more cookies!

Dear Mom and Dad,

Are you wondering why fourths didn't work out?

Bees!

One of the weed pullers got stung. They went on strike. We had to think again.

While we were thinking, we had a cartwheel contest. It was neat—I did half a cartwheel!

I was upside down when all of a sudden Judy said, "I know what we can do!"

Judy was all excited. "We can divide into eighths. There are eight girls in our bunk. So each girl is one-eighth of the group. We'll each be a team of one!"

What an excellent idea! That way everyone could do the job she likes best.

Naomi loves to sweep. So she did the floors. Toby and Jo like to scrub. They made the sink and shower shine. Judy is a dust demon. She even brought a feather duster to camp!

Every single person has a favorite job.

Now I like everything about camp—even cleaning up!

Your loving daughter,

Annie

P.S. I still won't like cleaning up at home!